RUAPEHU

KAREN
WILLIAMS

GODWIT

ERUPTS

THE RESTLESS MOUNTAIN

In 1995 and 1996 volcano lovers were treated to a touch of magic from a volcano lying at the heart of the central North Island of New Zealand. In September 1995 Ruapehu, the restless mountain, burst into life. The raw power of the ensuing eruptions captured world-wide attention, as towering columns of roiling ash and steam, torrential mud-flows and incandescent lava bombs presented an ongoing spectacle.

However, while locally spectacular, on a global scale and in terms of Ruapehu's formative history, this latest round of eruptions is insignificant. Mt St Helens' 1980 eruption was ten times bigger, and the climate-changing Philippine eruption of Mt Pinatubo in 1991 was up to 100 times larger than recent events at Ruapehu. But, unlike St Helens or Pinatubo, Ruapehu, the highest mountain in the North Island (2797 m), is an extremely popular outdoor playground, attracting hundreds of thousands of skiers, climbers and sightseers each year.

The volcanic trio of Ruapehu, Tongariro and Ngauruhoe, revered as places of power, are a part of the tribal identity of the Ngati Tuwharetoa and Ngati Rangi people who have lived in this area for centuries. In 1887, to protect these sacred mountains for all time, the paramount chief of Ngati Tuwharetoa, Te Heuheu Tukino IV, presented them to the Crown on condition they be set aside as a national park.

Tongariro National Park, declared a

World Heritage site in 1990, has become New Zealand's most-visited park. Slowly but steadily more people have settled in the area and a visitor-based industry has developed. The Whakapapa skifield including Iwikau ski lodges, Whakapapa Village, and Tukino and Turoa skifields have been built on the slopes of the volcano, and the small townships of Ohakune, National Park and the Turangi-Tongariro area now rely more and more on the skiers' dollar. With the ski seasons in both 1995 and 1996 seriously disrupted, the economic fallout for the area has been considerable, forcing a new generation to come to terms with the true nature of active volcanoes—they are bound to erupt, and Ruapehu is no exception.

Eruptions threatened skiing at Ruapehu for two years in a row.

A climber watches eruption clouds over Ruapehu from the summit of Ngauruhoe.

FIERY ORIGINS

Opposite:
Explosive eruptions
fling lava fragments
above Ruapehu's
crater.

Ruapehu, Ngauruhoe
and Tongariro form a
striking southern
terminus to the Taupo
Volcanic Zone.

Ruapehu and the other volcanoes of Tongariro National Park lie at the southern apex of the triangular-shaped Taupo Volcanic Zone. Since 1886, five volcanoes have been active in this 300-kilometre-long zone: White Island, Tarawera, Tongariro, Ngauruhoe and Ruapehu. In addition, numerous geothermal areas scattered throughout the zone share a similar origin.

New Zealand's volcanoes are part of the 'ring of fire', a chain of mountains that fringes the Pacific Ocean and includes approximately three-quarters of the world's active volcanoes. These volcanoes are a consequence of plate tectonics and occur along the collision zones of the spreading Pacific plate and the adjoining continental plates.

Underneath New Zealand, the Pacific plate collides with the Indo-Australian plate and is forced down into the mantle, a region of intense heat and enormous pressure. Although this process, called subduction, is continuing at a rate less rapid than the growth of a fingernail, it accounts for the fires that burn under many of the world's volcanoes.

Melting occurs along this collision zone, many kilometres below the surface, giving rise to a thick (viscous) mixture of gases and molten rock called magma. Weaknesses known as faults form in the Earth's crust where the two plates slide past each other. These faults allow the buoyant magma to move towards the surface.

The type of magma formed below Ruapehu is termed andesite. Typically, eruptions from andesite volcanoes such as Ruapehu tend to be explosive and small to medium-sized rather than cataclysmic events.

The gas component of Ruapehu's andesite magma is under high pressure and is normally released explosively as it nears the surface. This blows apart the molten rock, pulverising it to form masses of tiny fragments called ash and larger pieces of rock material. Occasionally the magma emerges more quietly as lava. In this way, over the last half a million years or so, the volcanic pile of Ruapehu, along with its volcano neighbours, has been built from successive layers of lava and ash.

THE CONTINUING STORY

Explosive eruptions have occurred frequently over a long period at Ruapehu from many vents. A crater lake 500 metres wide and containing about 10 million cubic metres of water usually occupies the current vent which is believed to have been active for about 2,500 years. The summit lake is heated volcanically yet is surrounded by glacial ice and snow. The temperature of the lake fluctuates, depending mainly on what is happening in the vent beneath.

Numerous small to medium-sized eruptions have been witnessed this century, ranging from minor emissions of steam and mud confined to Crater Lake, to the major events of 1945. During that phase, magma rose in the vent to gradually displace the lake. With the lake gone, explosive activity commenced and large ash eruptions continued for many months.

Ruapehu's crater lake is the major contributor to lahars. These are floods of water, mud, ash and other volcanic debris which flow down the sides of the volcano from time to time. They are normally caused by eruptions through the lake blasting water and mud onto the surrounding glaciers.

In 1953, collapse of a blockage at the lake outlet produced a major lahar from Ruapehu, resulting in the deaths of 151 people at Tangiwai. Since then, other lahars in the 1960s and 70s have damaged ski lifts and buildings, bridges and hydro-electric power facilities. Lahars remain the most serious hazard at Ruapehu. By mapping ancient and recent events and by putting in place monitoring equipment and warning systems, scientists, managers and ski operators continue to seek to understand the volcano and reduce the level of risk.

On rare occasions, when all is quiet, Ruapehu's Crater Lake has frozen over. In 1926, climbers stand in the centre of the frozen lake.

In 1945, lava reached the top of the active vent, spread across the crater floor and pushed out all the lake water. Powerful ash eruptions followed from a crater empty of water. Until 1995–96, this eruptive phase was considered to be New Zealand's largest this century.

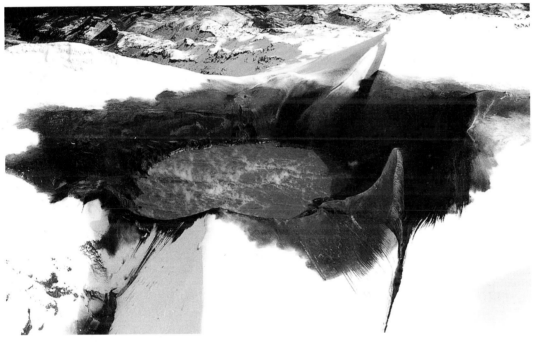

An ash eruption in April 1968 set off a lahar and darkened the summit of Ruapehu with ash.

A small explosive eruption occurred within the lake during an eruption sequence in May 1971.

Although traces of the earliest eruptions that gave birth to Ruapehu have been buried or obliterated by subsequent events, it is possible to piece together the history of the last quarter of a million years. Evidence can be seen on the mountain itself and in the surrounding landscape. This sequence, looking towards the Whakapapa side of the mountain, illustrates some of the key episodes that have shaped the Ruapehu of today.

P Pinnacle Ridge
C The Grand Chateau
W Whakapapa Skifield

250,000 years ago.
This early cone arose on the site of the present-day Ruapehu. Remnants of it survive as the Pinnacle Ridge (P), a series of jagged peaks dominating the skyline to one side of the Whakapapa skifield.

100,000 years ago.
As the millennia pass, new vents develop to the south and a larger cone grows to eventually dominate the now-eroded earlier cone. Massive lahars occur (1).

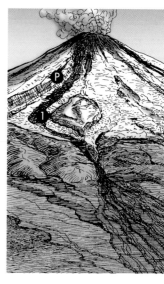

14,500 years ago.
Following further cone-building, glaciers advance down the mountain, eroding valleys, to almost reach the level of the present-day Grand Chateau. Huge lahars sweep down the slopes (1).

The cross-sections below show changes beneath Ruapehu's crater lake during 1994–95.

Pre-eruption late 1994.
Hot gases rise from a magma body up a rubble-filled 'pipe' beneath the vent containing Crater Lake. The lake heats up.

Late June 1995.
The magma body is destabilised, probably by the addition of new magma, and magma starts to move up the pipe.

29 June–23 September.
Explosive eruptions progressively clear the vent as pulses or rafts of magma reach the vent region. The largest of these occurs on 23 September.

25–30 September.
Following vent clearing, explosive activity becomes more continuous. Larger eruptions virtually empty the lake, producing major lahars down the Whangaehu Valley.

Mid-October.
Eruptions finally empty the lake. The main body of the magma column reaches the surface. Fountains of molten lava and bombs are ejected. Ash falls over the central and eastern North Island.

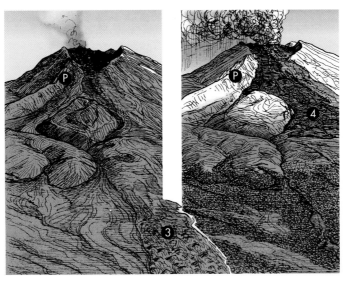

10,000 years ago.
Major eruptions produce huge avalanches of hot volcanic fragments (pyroclastic flows) (2).

9,500 years ago.
Flank collapse causes a giant landslide (3), which deposits debris onto the ring plain, forming the distinctive mounds beside the road to the Grand Chateau. (C)

9,000–5,000 years ago.
A new cone emerges and renewed activity sends lava pouring down the Whakapapa Valley (4).

Present-day Ruapehu.
Smaller scale but frequent explosive eruptions continue to emit ash and send lahars (1) down the flanks of the mountain.

Lifting the lid on today's landscape. These graphics locate some of the significant events that have shaped the mountains and the surrounding ring plain: huge lahars (1); pyroclastic flows (2); flank collapse (3); massive lava flows (4).

There have been many vents active in this area, and the most recent of these are shown in brighter colours.

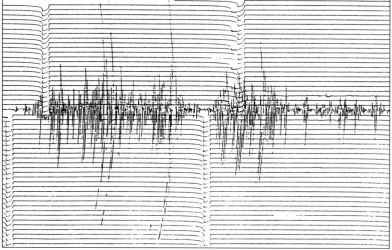

Eruptions on 18 and 20 September prompted scientists to fly to the crater lake to investigate.

On 23 September a spectacular eruption occurred from the lake. When the mountain blew at the end of a busy ski day, the awesome spectacle was witnessed by thousands of people on and about the volcano.

Large rocks, trailing white arcs of steam, were tossed up to a kilometre above the summit. Jets of black ash and sediment-laden water exploded upwards and outwards, to be engulfed by turbulent clouds of steam and ash rising vertically from the crater.

The eruptions jolted the seismograph at Whakapapa Village into a frenzy of activity as it recorded the activity beneath the volcano.

With eruptions continuing, the powerful lateral jets of hot water and debris triggered lahars (volcanic mudflows) down three major valleys. This unique photo sequence shows the progression of the fast-moving flows into the Whakapapaiti Valley. Ash turned the summit plateau grey and twin mudflows streaked the formerly pristine north-western slopes of Ruapehu.

One lahar sped down the southern boundary of the Whakapapa Ski Area at up to 90 kilometres per hour. Moments later, another surged into a nearby valley, narrowly missing the drive station of the Far West T-bar ski lift in the Whakapapaiti Valley.

Pages 16–17: Frequent large explosions continued to rock the mountain, producing more mudflows and ashfall.

On 25 September Ruapehu erupted again for several hours in two particularly impressive episodes. Explosions became more frequent until they were less than a minute apart.

Eruptions continued into the next day. Large pieces of lava (bombs and blocks), and masses of steam and other gases were ejected.

With the skifields and mountain roads closed, these eruptions were watched in safety from near The Grand Chateau.

The ongoing eruptions produced the most lahars recorded from Ruapehu in the past 130 years, dramatically lowering the level of Crater Lake. The biggest of these flowed down the Whangaehu Valley, the natural outlet for the lake, turning the river downstream into a wild torrent.

The heartbreaking scene following the Tangiwai rail disaster of 1953. A lahar from Ruapehu's crater lake surged down the Whangaehu River and washed away the railbridge. Only minutes later, an express train plunged into the river, killing 151 people.

The site of the Tangiwai tragedy in 1995, showing signs of the passage of the 20 or so lahars erupted from the lake between 18 September and 8 October.

The constant eruptions began to expose the interior of the active vent. With the lake all but empty, the style of eruptions changed and dark ash clouds were emitted at frequent intervals, blackening the ski slopes and bringing the 1995 season to a premature close.

In the biggest ashfall since 1945, ash was sprinkled over large areas of the central and eastern North Island.

Pages 24–25:
The sustained eruptions finally emptied the active vent of all water. For a short time around midnight on 11 October red-hot rocks fountained above the summit while lightning crackled in the dark plumes of ash. Molten ejecta were strewn up to three kilometres from the vent.

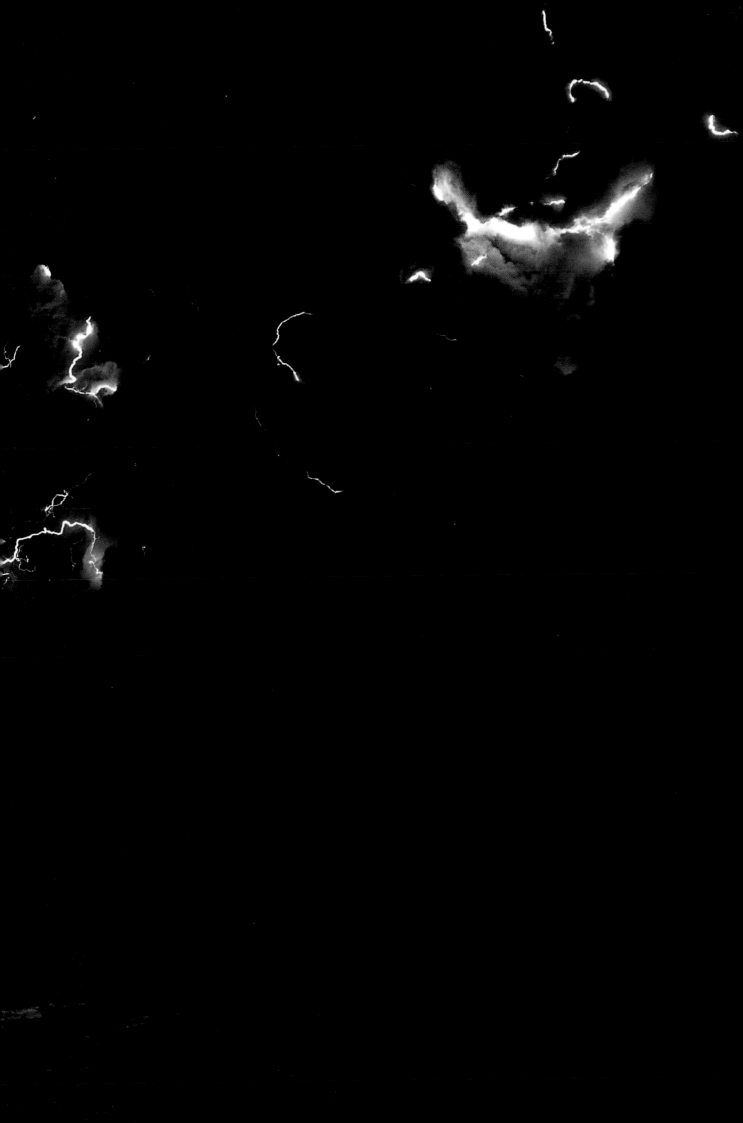

The eruptions of September and October hammered Dome Shelter, plastering it with debris. Although the exterior of the tiny emergency hut overlooking the crater was perforated by lava bombs, the sensitive monitoring equipment housed in the concrete-lined basement continued to operate, providing a valuable record for volcanologists.

As the ash eruptions eased, enormous amounts of gas began to stream from Ruapehu from mid-October and on into 1996. At times, the gas caused a pale blue-brown haze or volcanic smog known as 'vog', which drifted over large parts of the central and lower North Island.

Scientists ventured into the active crater to collect gas samples after the eruption. Gas output peaked at over 15,000 tonnes of sulphur dioxide a day—more than from erupting volcanoes elsewhere in the world.

In November a new lake began to form at the bottom of the active vent. Steaming fumaroles and bright yellow sulphur deposits can be seen on its shores, 100 metres below pre-eruption lake level.

With no major eruptions for over two months, the restrictions barring access to the summit area were lifted. In January and February 1996 thousands of people took the opportunity to view the desolate environment.

After a seven-month lull, innocent-looking pink clouds on 17 June 1996 were the first outward sign that eruptions were under-way again at Ruapehu. Intense volcanic tremor over the preceding two days had warned scientists that magma was rising again beneath the active vent.

Ruapehu rapidly cranked into full eruption mode, emitting threatening clouds of ash. Windows rattled in Whakapapa Village 10 kilometres away, and residents reported hearing noisy explosions. Perhaps a similar event long ago gave rise to the name Ruapehu, 'the explosive-sounding crater'.

The voluminous plume of ash seen from Rangipo on the Desert Road. The dense ash cloud blocked out the sun, keeping temperatures 5–10° C colder than expected.

The eruptions continued unabated all day and were a stunning sight from vantage points in the area.

Pages 36–37:
Coarse ash, similar to sand, rained out over the communities of the volcanic plateau, leaving deposits 1–5 millimetres thick. Poised to open for the winter ski season Ruapehu's skifields were once again the first-line casualties of the volcanic fallout as the cover of grit made the ski runs unusable.

The ash eruptions of 17 June had once again emptied the vent of water and left a deep coating of ash over the summit plateau, including Dome Shelter. That night for two hours molten lava, propelled by gases, was ejected in glowing sprays above the crater, peppering the summit region. This was accompanied by loud sonic booms.

Next day, bomb craters could be seen punched and melted into the snow by the red-hot material.

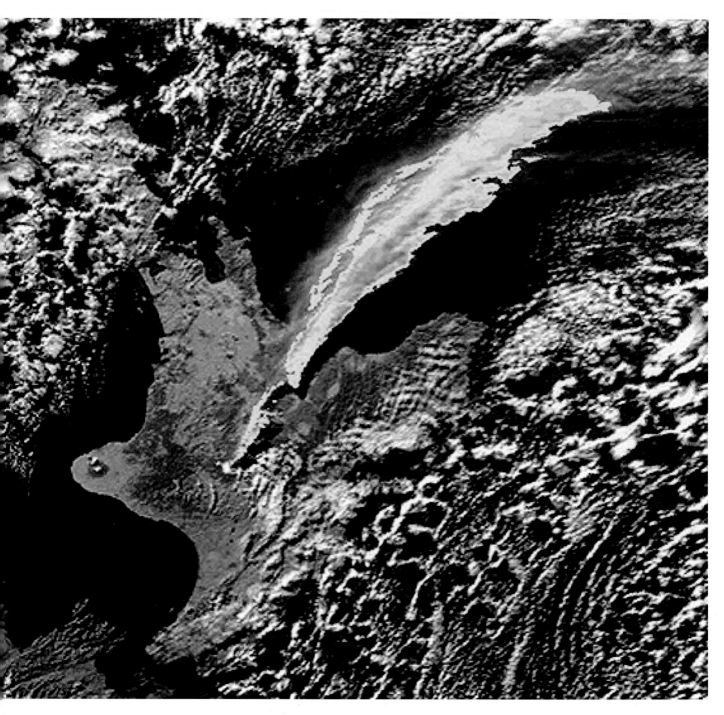

A remarkable view from space of a trail of volcanic ash over the North Island in mid-June. The ash plume is shown in false colour to enhance it. As ash can severely damage aircraft engines or stop them completely, a number of airports were closed for short periods in 1995 and 1996, affecting both local and international travellers.

While not life-threatening, the ash was a nuisance and caused some discomfort for those susceptible to respiratory and eye problems.

At times the Tongariro
River was turned grey
with ash and mudflow
debris, in startling
contrast to the clean
waters of Lake Taupo.

The silt-laden water
killed some adult trout
in the catchment but
fishing remained
excellent.

The 1995 breeding
season of the rare blue
duck was disrupted in
two of the three major
river systems around
the mountain.

The abrasive ash has
extensively damaged
turbines at the Rangipo
Power Station, halting
operations and costing
millions of dollars in
repairs.

Ash falling on
farmland provided free
fertiliser of sulphate
and some trace
elements, although it
caused some sheep and
deer deaths.

Moderate eruptions continued at Ruapehu into late July 1996, flinging incandescent rocks from the crater. Some of these projectiles triggered snow avalanches.

Ash eruptions interspersed with fresh snow built a potentially unstable snowpack of mixed layers and caused further avalanches.

The on-again off-again eruptions continued to coat the the ski areas with ash, disrupting the season for weeks and having a multi-million dollar impact on the local and regional economy.

The vegetation of Tongariro National Park and the nearby Kaimanawa Range has displayed a resilience to being showered in ash.

Ruapehu's two commercial skifields, Turoa Ski Resort and Whakapapa Ski Area, were able to open for business in August. Occasional eruptions into September continued to provide a fantastic backdrop and a reminder of the unpredictability of active volcanoes.

Photograph credits: Andris Apse, pp. 2–3; Ash Ansley, 12–13, 31 (right centre), 46–47 (4); Alan Bee, 4; John Chandler, 22 (bottom), 26 (top), 29 (top), 30 (bottom), 31 (top), 35 (2); Darrell Connelly, 34; Barbara Curtis, 27 (top), 32 (top left & right); Di Davies, 32 (bottom); Phil Doyle/*Sunday Star-Times*, 48; Gareth Eyres, 23, 30 (right); Lloyd Homer/ Institute of Geological and Nuclear Sciences, 6–7, 20 (top), 42–43; Tony Hughes, 1; Alastair Jamieson, 15 (top), 16–17, 21 (bottom), 29 (bottom), 30 (top left), 45 (top); Mark Jones, 31 (left); Helen Mitchell, 45 (bottom); Tim Mitchell, 31 (bottom right); Harry Keys/Karen Williams, 5, 12, 15 (bottom), 20 (bottom), 22 (top), 26 (bottom), 27 (bottom), 28, 30 (left centre), 33, 39 (2), 44 (2); *New Zealand Herald*, 21 (top), 38–39 (Nicola Topping), 42 (Russell Smith); Reuters New Zealand Ltd, 40; Craig Potton, 36–37; Ian Powell, 8; Michael Schneider, 24–25; Tongariro National Park collection, 9 (centre, bottom); *Wanganui Chronicle*, 41 (top); Noel Woodfield, 7, 14 (3), 18, 19 (3), 41 (bottom);

Art and digital imaging, pp. 10–11, Chris Gaskin, Bill and Jonathan Paynter.

The author and publisher are grateful to the photographers named above for their willing assistance and interest in the project. In addition, they would like to thank the following people who have helped in various ways: Scotty Barrie, Dave Mazey, Ruapehu Alpine Lifts; Bruce Clarkson, Landcare; Rhonda Dally, *Turangi Chronicle*; Walter de Bont; John Gibbs, Ross Martin, Glen McLean, Maureen Smith and Dave Wakelin, Department of Conservation; Angus Grimwade and Grant McMaster, Turoa Ski Resort; William Keys; Michelle McGill; Ian Nairn, Peter Otway, Institute of Geological and Nuclear Sciences; NIWA; Betty Wakelin, Tongariro High School. Finally, thanks to Chris Gaskin and Harry Keys for their special contributions to this book.

A GODWIT BOOK
published by
Random House New Zealand
18 Poland Road, Glenfield, Auckland, New Zealand

First published 1996

Reprinted 1996, 1997, 1998, 1999

© 1996 text, Karen Williams; illustrations, as credited above

The moral rights of the author have been asserted

ISBN 1 86962 004 6

Design: Martin Hill Design
Front cover photograph: Ash Ansley; back cover photograph: Noel Woodfield
Production: Kate Greenaway
Printed in Hong Kong